They divide into nine sections starting with Shrove Tuesday and Ash Wednesday, and finishing with Good Friday and Easter Day. 'Sharing Together', 'Prophecy Fulfilled', 'Forgiveness', 'Behold' and 'Father into Your hands' may be spread over the five weeks in-between.

Please look at the comments at the back of this book for some additional thoughts and ideas.

The Lent
Creative Retreat
ACTIVITY BOOK

With every blessing,

Mary and Mark Fleeson
Holy Island

Shrove Tuesday

Entering the Season of Lent can be an amazing journey of discovery, an opportunity to journey to the foot of the cross, to be challenged by the sacrifice and reassured by the resurrection.

Historically it is a time to fast and repent in preparation for the joyous celebration of Easter Day, the word shrove is the past tense of shrive, an old word that means to confess.

Across the world many traditions have emerged to help the faithful to prepare for the fasting aspect of Lent, many people enjoy pancakes or rich pastries, some countries have street processions and a party atmosphere (Fat Tuesday, Mardi Gras and Carnival).

At the root of all the celebrations is the idea of using up, and saying goodbye to, 'forbidden' foods such as fat, dairy and meat.

James encourages,
"Therefore confess your sins to each other and pray for each other so that you may be healed." (5:16)

Depending on the tradition you follow you may be very familiar with the idea of confession or it may be quite an alien concept, whatever your experience this is an ideal time to examine those things that burden us with guilt and let go of them completely.

**Talk and pray
with someone you trust**

or you could say the following:

Mighty God, I place into Your hands
the stuff that weighs me down,
the behaviour that offends You,
the times when I didn't act,
the times I turned away,
the burdens that I know I should not carry,
the blame I have no need to own.

Ash Wednesday

Lent begins on Ash Wednesday, it lasts for forty days and nights (Sundays aren't included).

Forty days are significant to the Christian and Judaic traditions, like the Hebrews of old Jesus spent forty days in the wilderness and Moses fasted forty days before receiving the Commandments.

In Churches all over the world ashes, which may be mixed with anointing oil, are daubed on the forehead in the shape of a cross.

They symbolise penitence, sorrow for ones sins and remind us that God made the first humans by breathing life into dust, without God we are nothing more than dust and our earthly bodies will eventually return to dust.

WHAT ARE YOU SORRY FOR?

What burdens can you give to God today, write one word in each box to remind you of what you must not take back!

Sharing Together

Meditation

One of the great things about the stories of Jesus is how beautifully human they are. At the last supper Jesus told his closest friends and followers that this would be the last time He would be with them and they, instead of making that time pleasant and companionable, argued amongst themselves, indulged in prideful boasts and displayed their preparedness for fighting despite Jesus' peaceful teaching. However, in their weakness they went on to risk all to be 'witnesses...to the ends of the earth.' (Acts 1:8)

Our Creator knows that we are far from perfect, that we will fall and fail but with God's help we can try again. Sharing a meal together in remembrance of that last supper is a step towards healing relationships and a step away from the bickering we are so prone to indulge in.

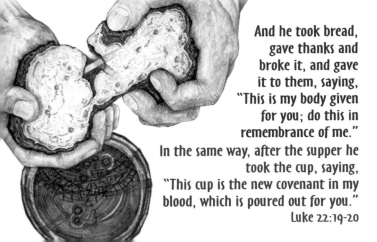

And he took bread,
gave thanks and
broke it, and gave
it to them, saying,
"This is my body given
for you; do this in
remembrance of me."
In the same way, after the supper he
took the cup, saying,
"This cup is the new covenant in my
blood, which is poured out for you."
Luke 22:19-20

He said to them, "... if you have a purse, take it, and also a bag; and if you don't have a sword, sell your cloak and buy one. It is written: 'And he was numbered with the transgressors'; and I tell you that this must be fulfilled in me. Yes, what is written about me is reaching its fulfilment."
Luke 22:36-37

Because he poured out his life unto death, and was numbered with the transgressors.
Isaiah 53:12

Meditation

Why did Jesus want his disciples to carry a sword? Surely it contradicts all that he taught about peace? He goes on to say that the two swords already being carried by the clearly wary disciples are enough and when Peter injures a servant of the high priest, a man called Malchus, in the garden, Jesus immediately heals him and says "No more!"

Jesus grew up with full knowledge of the prophetic books of the Nevi'im, the prophetic middle section of the Tanakh, the Jewish Bible, He would have known Isaiah's words by heart and He would have known that He was to fulfil the God-given prophecies. But how to do that when His mission had been peaceful? He needed to give them a sound reason to convict Him, peaceful preaching wasn't enough to warrant arrest but His followers committing a violent act with a weapon against the Sanhedrin was.

In the last days, God says, "I will pour out my Spirit on all people. Your sons and daughters will prophesy, your young will see visions, your old will dream dreams."

Acts 2:17

Forgiveness

Then Jesus said,
"Father, forgive them, for they do not know what they do."

Luke 23:34

Have you ever been stopped in your tracks by what a friend of mine used to call 'cringes'? Flashback memories of things you wish you hadn't done or said or that you wish you had done differently? If memories continue to 'haunt' you then the situations may not have ever been resolved.

Forgiveness isn't easy, I suspect that our human nature desires more to gain revenge than to forgive, forgiveness isn't something we can do in our own strength.

Follow one of the knots on the next page with your finger and pause where it crosses. When you pause think about the cringes that remain, the mistakes that haunt us when we're tired and low, the things we thought we had let go of but somehow they continue to stifle us.

Say out loud,
"With God's help I release these memories and I forgive myself and [n]."

Follow the other knot with your finger and pause where it crosses. When you pause think about someone who has hurt you in some way.

Say out loud,
"With God's help I forgive [n] and I ask for Your healing."

[n] = name of person

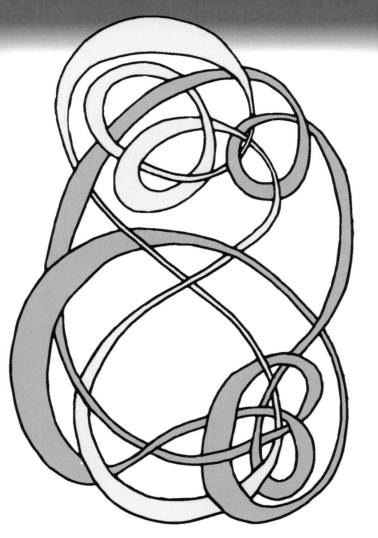

Behold your Son

Behold your Mother

Meditation

While the principalities and powers believe they are tearing his family apart, Jesus is quietly putting it together again: this mother with this son, this past with this future.

Although his enemies will succeed in killing him, he will leave no orphans behind. At the foot of the cross, the mother of the old becomes the mother of the new. The beloved disciple becomes her new beloved son.

When Jesus saw his mother there, and the disciple whom he loved standing nearby, he said to her,

"Woman, here is your son,"

and to the disciple,

"Here is your mother."

From that time on, this disciple took her into his home.

John 19:26-27

Father into Your hands

It was now about noon, and darkness came over the whole land until three in the afternoon, for the sun stopped shining. And the curtain of the temple was torn in two.

Luke 23:44-45

Jesus called out with a loud voice, "Father, into your hands I commit my spirit."

Luke 23:46

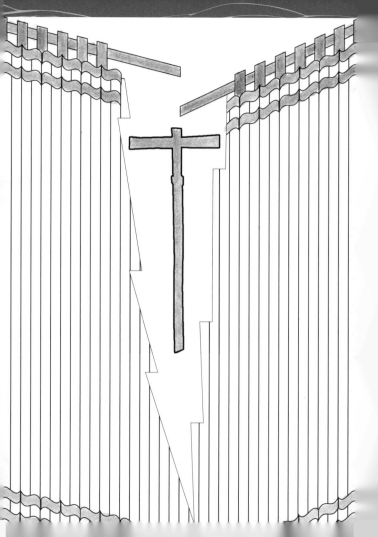

Easter Day

He is not here; He has risen!

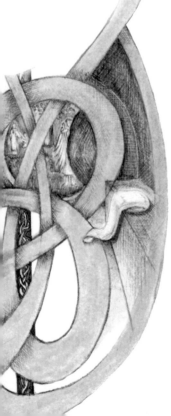

"But...the Holy Spirit, whom the Father will send in my name, will teach you all things and will remind you of everything I have said to you."

John 14:26

You may be very familiar with the idea of inviting the Holy Spirit into your life. You may have done it once and felt that was enough. In one sense once is enough, but it is easy to forget the power of the gift of the Holy Spirit and all that it offers us.

When you invite the Holy Spirit to act in your daily life you are asking God

to LOVE you
- Romans 5:5
to give you JOY
- 1Thessalonians 1:6
to COMFORT you
- John 14:27/Philippians 4:7
to ENABLE you
- Titus 3:4-7
to CHALLENGE you
- Romans 12:1-2

Opposite is a prayer,
say it often and expect to be changed

Creator of all things
immense and invisible
and everything in-between,
Creator of me,
Hear my call.

Send Your Spirit into my
heart, I bind it there to
teach me how to love,

Send Your Spirit into my
mind, I bind it there to
guide me,

Send Your Spirit into my
body, I bind it there to
sustain me.

Creator God, Hear my call.

Comments and Encouragements

Take time out. Just ten minutes a day or half an hour twice a week set aside purely for being in God's presence can make a big difference to how your spiritual life grows. Find a quiet place and give the time you have to God, you could use the prayer in the Sunrise section of this book.

Pray like it's as vital as breathing. Sometimes we place praying, like God, into a box. We think God can only be met or talked to in Church or when a certain person is present, in reality we were created to communicate with our Creator, to enjoy a two-way conversation which never ends. There's so much God wants to share with us, to show us and teach us, so pray constantly and be aware of Gods presence in all things.

Look for God in the small things. The snatched conversation you just had with the shop assistant, God was there; the hug you gave your grieving friend, God was there; the moment you took to smell the flowers, God was there; when you washed up after dinner, God was there. It isn't that God wants to do the washing up for you or promise you that every washing up moment will be filled with joy but God may be telling you that if you spend those times that need little thought, in prayer and conversation with your Creator, then your life may be that bit richer and purposeful.

I should point out that if you don't pray during the washing up your life will not fall apart, I know that sometimes I'm so tired that I can't even form a coherent thought let alone pray sensibly and a few minutes of mindless washing up is a pleasurable chance to switch off. If you can't pray then try singing or humming and just be open to whatever God may want to say to you.

Never 'beat yourself up' for not doing enough, practice just being and be available when God calls you to do something.

Allow yourself to be vulnerable to others and to God. It's not easy to do but when we allow others to see our true selves they will see more of God and God will be able to use you more effectively to help others.